Sweet Dreams & Moonbeams

8501 West Higgins Road, Suite 300, Chicago, Illinois 60631
Lower Ground Floor, 59 Gloucester Place, London W1U 8JJ

www.pikidsmedia.com

8 7 6 5 4 3 2 1
Manufactured in China.

Sweet Dreams and Moonbeams

Sweet dreams and moonbeams
shine over you, my dear.
All the world has gone to bed
now that night is here.

Lullaby and Goodnight

Lullaby and good night,
Put your head down and sleep tight.
Lie down now and rest,
May your slumber be blessed.

Diddle, Diddle, Dumpling

Diddle, diddle, dumpling,
My son John
Went to bed with his trousers on.
One shoe off, and one shoe on,
Diddle, diddle, dumpling,
My son John.

Hush Little Baby

Hush, little baby,
Don't say a word.
Mama's going to buy you
A mockingbird.
And if that mockingbird
Won't sing,
Mama's going to buy you
A diamond ring.

Wee Willie Winkie

Wee Willie Winkie
Runs through the town,
Upstairs and downstairs
In his nightgown.
Rapping at the window,
Crying through the lock,
“Are the children all in bed?
Now it’s eight o’clock.”

Rock-a-bye, baby,
On the treetop.
When the wind blows,
The cradle will rock.
When the bough breaks,
The cradle will fall.
Down will come baby,
Cradle and all.

Man in the Moon

The man in the moon,
Looked out of the moon,
Looked out of the moon and said,
"It's time that now I'm getting up,
All children are in bed."

Star Light, Star Bright

Star light, star bright,
First star I see tonight,
I wish I may,
I wish I might,
Have the wish,
I wish tonight.

Sleep Baby Sleep

Sleep, baby, sleep.
Your father guards the sheep.
Your mother shakes the dreamland tree,
And from it fall sweet dreams for thee.
Sleep, baby, sleep.

I See the Moon

I see the moon,
And the moon sees me.
The moon sees somebody I'd like to see.
Please bless the moon,
And please bless me.
Please bless the somebody I'd like to see.

Good night,
Sleep tight,
Don't let the bedbugs bite.